Animal Rescue Shelter

written by Jay Dale

illustrated by Wesley Lowe

Engage Literacy is published in 2013 by Raintree.
Raintree is an imprint of Capstone Global Library Limited, a company
incorporated in Engand and Wales having its registered office at 7 Pilgrim
Street, London, EC4V 6LB – Registered company number: 6695582
www.raintreepublishers.co.uk

Originally published in Australia by Hinkler Education, a division
of Hinkler Books Pty Ltd.
Text copyright © UpLoad Publishing Pty Ltd 2012
Illustration copyright © Hinkler Books Pty Ltd 2012

Written by Jay Dale
Lead authors Jay Dale and Anne Giulieri
Cover illustration and illustrations by Wesley Lowe
Illustrations on p 24 by Gaston Vanzet
Edited by Gwenda Smyth
UK edition edited by Dan Nunn, Catherine Veitch and Sian Smith
Designed by Susannah Low, Butterflyrocket Design

Animal Rescue Shelter
ISBN: 978 1 406 26507 1
10 9 8 7 6 5 4 3 2 1

Printed and bound in China by Leo Paper Products Ltd

About Me

Name: Jimmy Scott

Age: 8 years old

Birthday: 24th of June

Pets: a rabbit called Buster

Hobbies: riding bikes, reading about animals, helping at Mrs Rosso's Animal Rescue Shelter

What I want to be when I grow up: a vet

Dear Aunty Pam,

I have something special to tell you.
Mum and I have become helpers
at the *Animal Rescue Shelter*.
The shelter is only a ten-minute walk
from our house.

At the shelter they have
many different animals.
They have dogs, cats, rabbits,
ducks and chickens.

Most of the animals
come to the shelter
because they're lost,
or they're not wanted any more.
Some of the animals were found
walking around the streets.
They were hungry and frightened.

Mrs Rosso, who runs the shelter,
is a really kind woman.
She takes care of all the animals
as if they were her own.
She *grooms* the dogs with a *brush*
and cleans out the animal pens.
She tries to take each dog
for a walk every day.

It's very hard for Mrs Rosso to take care
of all the animals by herself.
That's why Mum and I wanted to help her.

We help at the shelter every Saturday.
There are lots of other helpers, too.
Most of the helpers are older people,
but there are teenagers who help out as well.
All the helpers are very kind to the animals.

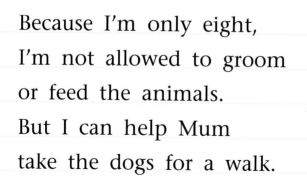

Because I'm only eight,
I'm not allowed to groom
or feed the animals.
But I can help Mum
take the dogs for a walk.

Mrs Rosso also lets me go
into the *chicken coop*
and gather the eggs from the hens.

Sometimes baby animals are born at the shelter.
Last week some kittens were born.
They were very sweet.
Mrs Rosso said she'll let me play with the baby kittens when they're old enough.

Every weekend lots of people
come to look at the animals.
Most of them are looking
for a new pet to take home.
It makes Mum and me really happy
when a dog or a cat
finds a new place to live.

Mrs Rosso makes sure that the new owners
will give the animals a good home.
She talks to them about where
their new animal will sleep,
how to groom it and what to feed it.

Two weeks ago, an old dog called Stumpy was taken home by a man called Mr Ray. Stumpy had been at the shelter for six weeks.

That's a long time for an animal to be there. Most of the animals find a home right away. Mrs Rosso said Mr Ray and Stumpy were a good match because they both needed a friend.

Some people don't have time to work
at the shelter like Mum and me,
so they give money, old *blankets*
or food for the animals.
My friend's family gave Mrs Rosso
some blankets and Dad gave
some *money* to buy pet food.

Next Saturday all the helpers are setting up a *fair* at the shelter.

There will be *pony* rides, and cakes and sweets to buy.

We're all hoping to make lots of money for the shelter.

Mrs Rosso will then be able to build a new coop for the chickens.

Maybe you, and some of your friends, might like to come to the fair.

Mum and I really enjoy the work we do
at the animal shelter.
I hope you'll be able to come next Saturday.
You might find yourself a new pet
to take home!

Lots of love,
Jimmy

Picture glossary

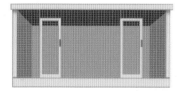

Animal Rescue Shelter

fair

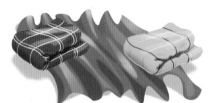

blankets

grooms

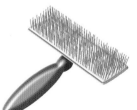

brush

money

chicken coop

pony

Boats

written by Wendy Graham

Engage Literacy is published in 2013 by Raintree.
Raintree is an imprint of Capstone Global Library Limited, a company
incorporated in Engand and Wales having its registered office at 7 Pilgrim
Street, London, EC4V 6LB – Registered company number: 6695582
www.raintreepublishers.co.uk

Originally published in Australia by Hinkler Education, a division
of Hinkler Books Pty Ltd.
Text and illustration copyright © Hinkler Books Pty Ltd 2012

Written by Wendy Graham
Lead authors Jay Dale and Anne Giulieri
Illustrations pp 6, 11, 23–24 by Gaston Vanzet
Edited by Gwenda Smyth
UK edition edited by Dan Nunn, Catherine Veitch and Sian Smith
Designed by Susannah Low, Butterflyrocket Design

Boats
ISBN: 978 1 406 26543 9
10 9 8 7 6 5 4 3 2 1

Printed and bound in China by Leo Paper Products Ltd

Acknowledgements
Cover images (left to right): iStockphoto.com/ © James Steidl; © Veronica Wools | Dreamstime.com;
© Yuriykulik | Dreamstime.com; Glow Images/Prisma/Otto Werner.; p4 top (and title page): © Veronica Wools
| Dreamstime.com; p4 second from top: © Gordan Poropat | Dreamstime.com; p4 middle: © Ivan Cholakov
| Dreamstime.com; p4 bottom left: © Nadiya Kravchenko | Dreamstime.com; p4 bottom right (and Contents
page top): © Alptraum | Dreamstime.com; p5 top: © Baloncici | Dreamstime.com; p5 bottom: © Felics |
Dreamstime.com; p6 top right: © Dalibor Sevaljevic | Dreamstime.com; p7 top left: iStockphoto.com/ © Damir
Spanic; p7 top right: iStockphoto.com/ © Brian Palmer; p7 bottom: Glow Images/ © Ariel Skelley/CORBIS;
p8: Getty Images/Stockbyte; p9 top left: Glow Images/Prisma/Otto Werner; p9 top right: © Age Fotostock /
SuperStock; p9 bottom: © Lianem | Dreamstime.com; p10: © Glenda Powers | Dreamstime.com; p12 top
(and Contents page bottom): © Yuriykulik | Dreamstime.com; p12 middle: © Tom Dowd | Dreamstime.com;
p12 bottom: Onne van der Wal / Bluegreenpictures.com; p13 top: © Gina Smith | Dreamstime.com;
p13 middle: iStockphoto.com/ © Brian Palmer; p13 bottom: © Will Iredale | Dreamstime.com; p14:
© Newspix / News Ltd / James Kerr; p15 top: Imagebroker.net/SuperStock; p15 middle: © Julie Feinstein |
Dreamstime.com; p15 bottom: iStockphoto.com/ © egdigital; p16 top: © Jennifer Pitiquen | Dreamstime.com;
p16 middle: © Sanches1980 | Dreamstime.com; p16 bottom: © Nigel Spiers | Dreamstime.com;
p17 top: iStockphoto.com/ © David Joyner; p17 middle: © Sebastian Czapnik | Dreamstime.com;
p17 bottom: Courtesy Irish Ferries; p18 top: © Michele Cornelius | Dreamstime.com; p18 bottom: iStockphoto.
com/ © Peter Leyden; p19 top left: © Nattesha | Dreamstime.com; p19 top right: Tetra Images/SuperStock;
p19 bottom: Transtock/SuperStock; p20: iStockphoto.com/ © choicegraphx; p21 left (and back cover):
iStockphoto.com/ © Dan Barnes; p21 right: iStockphoto.com/ © Oytun Karadayi; p22 left: iStockphoto.com/
© James Steidl; p22 right: © Alex Zarubin | Dreamstime.com; p23 top left: © Farek | Dreamstime.com;
p23 top right: © Alvera | Dreamstime.com; p23 bottom left: © Marzanna Syncerz | Dreamstime.com;
p23 bottom right: © Kostyantyn Ratnikov | Dreamstime.com

Contents

Introduction

There are many different
kinds of boats.
Some boats, such as sailing boats,
need wind in their sails to move.
Large ships, however,
use *powerful engines*
to move through the sea.

Some boats are used for fun,
for travel or for fishing.
Others are used for work
or to move *goods*
from place to place.

In this book, you will read about
many different kinds of boats.

There are about
38,000 ships or boats
on the world's oceans
at any one time.

These boats are safe in this *port* while
they are not out in the open sea.

5

Fishing Boats

There are many different kinds of fishing boats. Some fishing boats are small and have *benches* for people to sit on. These boats use a small motor to move through the sea.

Some fishing boats are small enough to go on a car's roof.

Some small fishing boats are made of metal while others are made of wood.

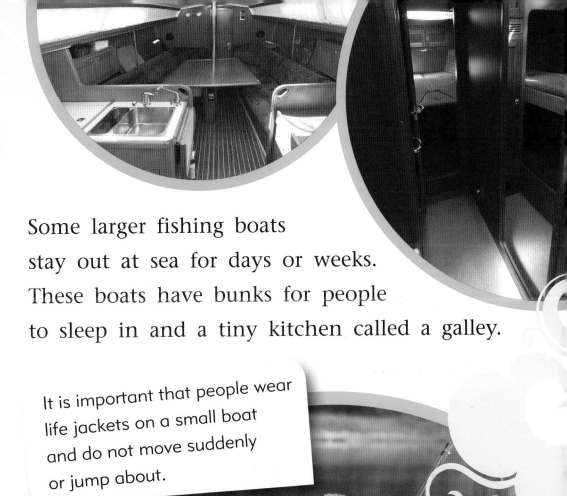

Some larger fishing boats stay out at sea for days or weeks. These boats have bunks for people to sleep in and a tiny kitchen called a galley.

It is important that people wear life jackets on a small boat and do not move suddenly or jump about.

Trawlers

Some people's job is to catch fish.
They use a boat called a *trawler*.
Trawlers pull special nets
through the sea to catch fish.
Some trawlers are small boats
while others are large.
They have an engine room,
bunks and a galley.

Large fishing trawlers
catch lots of fish
in their nets.

Some trawlers have special *machines* for lifting heavy nets full of fish up onto the *deck*.

Fish that are caught are kept cold in ice or seawater.

Sailing Boats

Some people enjoy sailing for fun. A sailing boat skims across the top of the water. When the wind hits its sails, the boat is pushed along.

People sail for sport, too. You can race sailing boats all year round. People can go to sailing school to learn how to sail.

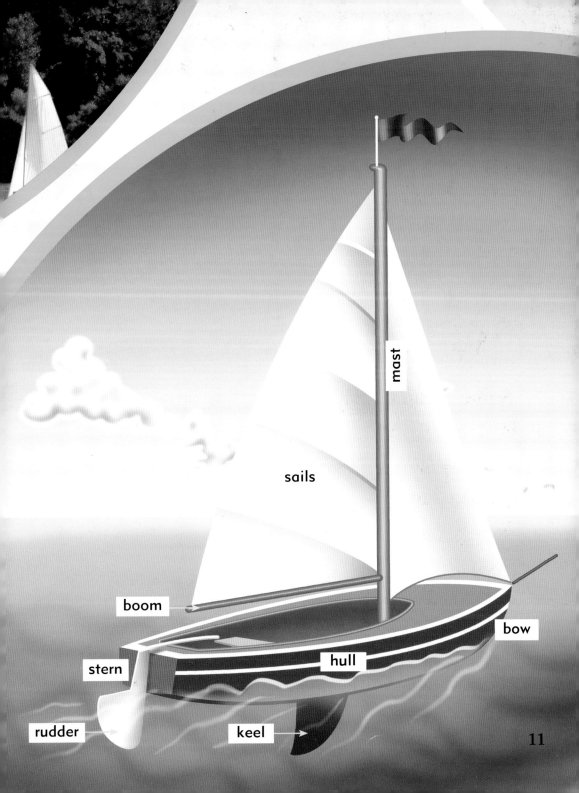

mast

sails

boom

bow

stern

hull

rudder

keel

11

Yachts

Large sailing boats
are called yachts.
They are light and fast-moving.
The wind in their sails
moves them across the sea.
Some people race their yachts.

Sometimes people use
their yacht as their home
when they travel
from place to place.

A very large yacht is called
a mega sailing yacht.
It has many cabins and
can carry up to 50 people.

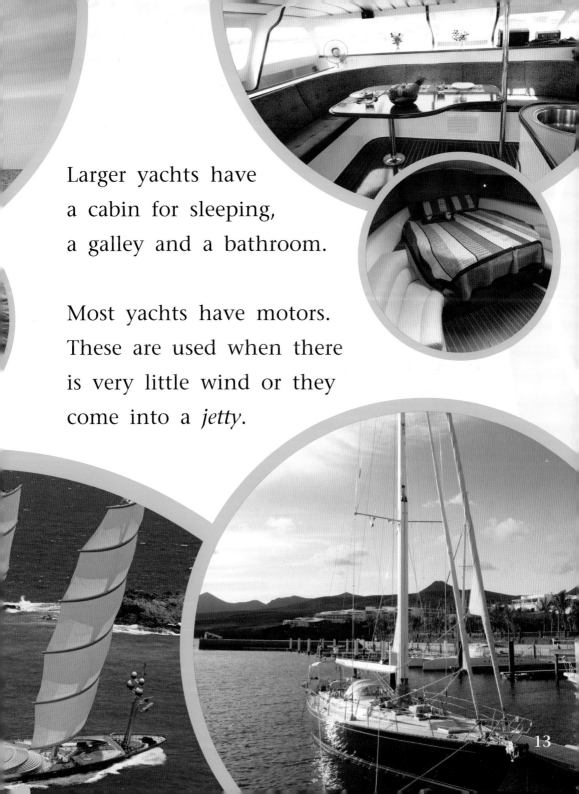

Larger yachts have
a cabin for sleeping,
a galley and a bathroom.

Most yachts have motors.
These are used when there
is very little wind or they
come into a *jetty*.

Police Boats

Some police officers work on police boats. Police boats have very powerful engines, so they can move swiftly across the water. Police boats have *sirens* and flashing lights just like police cars.

Some police boats have police divers who dive underwater.

Police officers on police boats work very hard to keep our waters safe.

Most large cities with ports have police boats.

Most police boats are very fast!

Water Taxis

Water taxis are boats that take people a short distance across the water. They might carry a few people or they might carry as many as 40 people. The seating area is sometimes covered so people do not get wet in rainy weather. There are also outside areas where people can enjoy the sunshine.

Water taxis can be used to take people to work, to an island or to a boat.

Some water taxis can land right on the beach.

Ferries

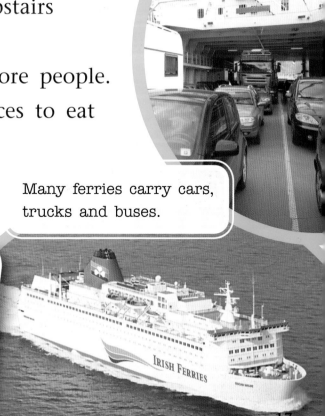

Ferries are much larger than water taxis. They carry a large number of people from one place to another. Ferries usually arrive and leave at the same time every day. Some ferries have upstairs and downstairs areas so they can carry more people. Some even have places to eat and cabins where people can sleep.

Many ferries carry cars, trucks and buses.

The world's largest ferry is called a superferry. It can carry about 1340 cars, 240 trucks and 2000 people.

IRISH FERRIES

Tugboats

Even though tugboats
are small, they are very powerful.
They push or tow boats
that cannot move under their own power.
Sometimes, when a boat is stuck
in *shallow* water, a tugboat will pull it out.
Most tugboats have a *crew* of four people.

Small tugboats can
tow huge ships
in or out of a busy port.

Tugs are so strongly
built that they can be
used as ice-breakers.
Ice-breakers are boats
that push through
water that is full of ice.

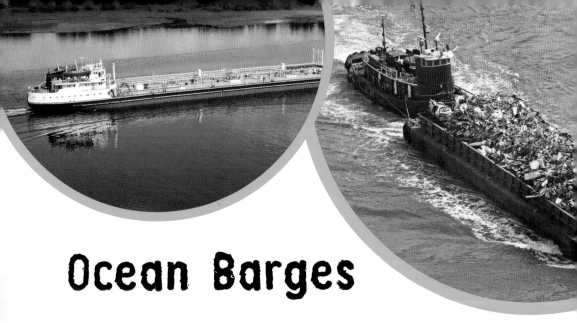

Ocean Barges

Most ocean barges have a large, flat deck. They carry all kinds of things such as cars, *machinery*, rubbish and other heavy items.

Other ocean barges do special jobs such as *dredging* or laying pipes beneath the sea.

Cargo Ships

Cargo ships move goods
such as furniture, cars and food
to different parts of the world.

Cargo ships are also called
container ships.

Containers are giant metal boxes
that hold goods for transport.
The containers can hold many different
kinds of goods such as clothes or TV sets.
These are loaded onto the cargo ship
at a place called a port.

One cargo ship
can carry
many containers.

Ocean Liners

Many people go on ocean liners for holidays. Ocean liners are sometimes called cruise ships. They travel all around the world. These large ships have *restaurants*, swimming pools and even *cinemas*. There are often thousands of people on board.

Ocean liners have many decks with cabins for sleeping.